YOUR DARTMOOR CENTURY

100 things to discover on Dartmoor

Thought up by
John Hayward

Curlew Publications

First published
by Curlew Publications
All rights reserved
© Copyright John Hayward 1989

Other works by the author:
   A New Key to Wild Flowers, 1987
   101 Dartmoor Letterboxes, 1988
   Illustrations to Exploring Dartmoor by F. H. Starkey, 1988
   An Hour's Stroll on Dartmoor, 1988

ISBN 0 9514037 1 0

Typeset by *Exe Valley Dataset Ltd*, Exeter, Devon
Printed and bound by *A. Wheaton & Co. Ltd*, Exeter, Devon

Contents

READ THESE TWO PAGES
BEFORE YOU START YOUR DISCOVERIES

In this book are 100 things for you to find on Dartmoor.

There are some very easy ones that you will see almost every time you go for a walk on the Moor. But to find the rest you will have to keep your eyes open, study the rocks and landscape, and look carefully at the plants and birds.

During an hour's walk almost anywhere on the Moor you should be able to collect several new ones.

Just a few are quite difficult. You may have to kneel down to study them properly. For instance, a small blue flower in the grass may not be common Bird's-eye or Milkwort (which are not in this hundred), but the rarer Ivy-leaved Bellflower (No. 51).

The 'ONLY ONE' section contains well known and interesting things, of which there is only one on Dartmoor, so you will have to make a special trip to see those. But you will certainly find many others on the way.

There are only two things in this book (the last two) for which you will have to go on to a firing range. That of course is easy, for the Okehampton range is open for most of the school holidays and every weekend. But to find a peat pass (No. 99) is a real challenge. Only try it if the weather is clear and settled, and you have someone with you who knows how to navigate with map and compass.

Just in case you cannot manage this then do Number 101 instead.

The clues to several things tell you to look at a map. This always means to the 'Outdoor Leisure' map of Dartmoor, the one with a yellow cover. It is by far the best map for walkers.

THINGS TO DO: When you make a discovery fill in the place and date at the bottom of the page, and perhaps also colour the NUMBER and NAME boxes at the top.

Then colour the same numbered square on page 107. This chart will then show how your collection is growing.

WHEN YOU HAVE FILLED IN 100 SQUARES

you will be quite an expert
about Dartmoor

LEAT

Devonport Leat

For hundreds of years the only source of power on the Moor was water. So this had to be brought from a river to where it was needed along a specially dug channel called a leat. Then it could turn a wheel or supply water to a farm. Some of the leats run for miles and you can see the lines of old dry ones along many hillsides.

For this book you should only count a leat which is still flowing.

CLUES: The Devonport Leat runs into Burrator Reservoir, the Holne Moor Leat round Combestone Tor.

I walked along the . . . . leat

near . . . . on . . . .

AQUEDUCT

The Devonport leat crosses the River Meavy

When a leat was dug to take water to a mine or farm or mill it sometimes had to cross a valley down which a stream was flowing. This meant building an aqueduct (a bridge to carry water) across the stream. If you walk along a running leat you will come across lots of very small aqueducts, but try to visit one where you can name the stream which the aqueduct crosses.

CLUES: There is one not far from the car park on Barn Hill, or the one illustrated above, or . . . .

I walked along the . . . . leat

aqueduct over the River . . . .

on . . . .

7

CLAPPER

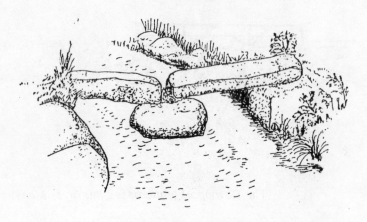

A small clapper bridge near Babeny

A clapper is a slab of granite placed on two boulders to cross a stream or leat. A clapper bridge may have up to about six such slabs. The best known of the big ones spans the East Dart at Postbridge. It has probably been there for about 500 years. Two other big ones, at Bellever and Dartmeet, have been partly washed away, but hundreds of small ones are left for you to discover.

CLUES: Almost any flowing leat will have some clappers across it.

I crossed a clapper over the . . . .

near . . . . on . . . .

This is a nearly-but-not-quite sort of bridge. A wide deep leat running round a hillside forms a barrier to animals, just as a wall does. But sometimes a farmer may want his sheep to graze on both sides of a leat. So he arranges two slabs of granite projecting towards each other from opposite banks. Sheep (and humans) can then jump across. These would be easier to put in place than even a small clapper.

CLUES: Walk along a running leat (such as the Devonport Leat) to find one.

I jumped across a sheep-leap over the . . . .

. . . . leat near . . . .

on . . . .

SLUICE

The Devonport Leat comes down Raddick Hill

A sluice is a kind of gate built across a stream or leat. It slides, or is wound, up and down to regulate the amount of water that can pass beneath it. If a sluice is built across a leat there will be an overflow channel on the upstream side.

Always remember that the water in a running leat may be a vital supply to a farm, so never do anything to interrupt the flow.

CLUES: Just walk up any flowing leat.

I found a sluice . . . .

. . . . on . . . .

Along the Grimstone and Sortridge Leat

Here is another way of regulating a flow of water. It is simply an oblong block of granite with a hole an inch in diameter drilled through it. The block is set in the leatside so that water can escape through the hole. The bull's-eye is placed so as to let water into a side leat that branches off a main one. Some have become submerged over the years and you will have to feel for the hole under water.

CLUES: The one illustrated is near Windy Post.

I saw a Bull's-eye stone in the . . . .

. . . . leat on . . . .

Here the Abbots' Way crosses the Plym

For thousands of years travellers over the Moor have searched for fords to cross streams and rivers. But finding a shallow stretch where the riverbed is sandy or stony, the banks are firm, and the approach is suitable for both horses and pedestrians, is not easy. So safe fords were well used, and almost all of them can still be plainly seen.

CLUES: Try any well marked track that seems to be heading across a valley.

I came to a ford across the . . . .

near . . . . on . . . .

STEPPING STONES

At Week Ford on the West Dart

It is great fun to cross a river on stepping stones, but look carefully at each one before you jump on to it, and never be in a hurry. On many Dartmoor rivers stepping stones are to be found beside a ford, but even these may be under water for much of the year.

CLUES: Ford and stepping stones often go together.

I came to some stepping stones across the

River . . . . at . . . .

on . . . .

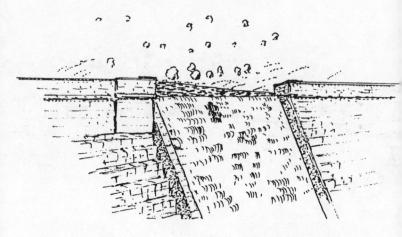

Fernworthy Dam

Most of the water in a reservoir leaves through underground pipes, and you don't see it again until you turn on a tap at home. But when a reservoir is full the water falls out through the spillway in the dam, and cascades down the outside. The best place to stand is at the bottom where you can watch the water falling towards you. Unfortunately not all the Dartmoor dams have a path round the bottom.

CLUES: Good ones are Avon and Fernworthy, especially after a wet spell.

I watched the water falling down the spillway at

. . . . on . . . .

GROUNDER

Grounders are the huge boulders that are sometimes built into the base of drystone walls. With enormous effort the wall builders levered them out of the ground nearby, and with much heaving and pushing moved them into position. A well maintained wall with a big grounder every few yards is a work of art (as well as science). Stand and admire it.

CLUES: A grounder is very much bigger than the other stones.

I saw some grounders in a wall near . . . .

. . . . on . . . .

WALL STILE

A lot of hard work goes into building a drystone wall, but once a few stones have been dislodged the wall is no longer stockproof. So never try to climb over a wall that is in good repair. The result could well be fallen stones, a broken leg, and an angry farmer. When a public footpath crosses an enclosure you may find, as well a gate, a stile like the one above. Climb over it to see how it is made.

CLUES: They are usually on high walls.

I crossed a wall stile near . . . .

. . . . on . . . .

Cattle, ponies and sheep often graze together. Sometimes a farmer would want his sheep to be able to go into another pasture, but not the larger animals. So he would build a low tunnel through the field wall that only the sheep could use. These tunnels are called 'sheep creeps'.

CLUES: If you walk up from the road to see 'The Ten Commandments' you will pass one. There is another in the wall beyond the Longstone on Merrivale Down.

I saw a sheep creep near . . . .

. . . . on . . . .

These posts made it quick and easy to close the 'gate' after cattle or a cart had been driven through. No iron fittings or cords were needed, yet they were quite stock-proof. When you find a pair decide which post you would slot the planks into first.

CLUES: An easy pair to find is in a car park near a well known bridge.

I saw a pair of slotted gateposts at . . . .

. . . . on . . . .

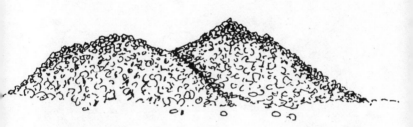

Wittaburrow Cairn

These are huge prehistoric piles of stones. The best ones are on hilltops and they show up from far away like a pimple on the skyline. Some are thought to have been burial places. The stones are loose so climb the pile carefully.

CLUES: They are marked on the map, even many of the small ones. Here are some easy ones to visit: Cox Tor, Yar Tor, Rippon Tor. There are more exciting ones on Yes Tor or Eastern White Barrow.

I climbed the cairn on . . . .

. . . . on . . . .

Round about 3,000 years ago Dartmoor's climate was better than it is now, and there were many hundreds of small homes on the hills, sometimes just a few together, sometimes twenty or more with a wall round the whole group. These are often marked on the map as 'settlements'. Grimspound is a well known one but there are many others. When you find a hut circle imagine it with a pole in the centre and a thatched roof.

CLUES: The map will show you the site of many hut circles.

I visited a hut circle near . . . .

. . . . on . . . .

STONE CIRCLE

The Nine Maidens of Belstone Tor

These circles of standing stones are quite a mystery. No one knows what they were used for, when, why, or by whom they were built. A few of them have probably been there for between 3,000 and 4,000 years. There are about a dozen large circles on the Moor, but in some cases many of the stones have disappeared.

CLUES: 'The Nine Maidens' are easy to visit, but if you would like to see a grander circle go to Scorhill.

I visited the stone circle near . . . .

. . . . on . . . . I counted . . . . . . stones.

21

*Part of
the row
on Stalldown
Barrow*

Another mystery of the Moor. You could have fun inventing a theory of your own to explain what these rows are for. There are short rows, long rows, single rows, double rows, treble rows, level rows, uphill and downhill rows, rows all alone and rows with other ones. Whichever one you find walk all along it (except perhaps the one that is 2 miles long!).

CLUES: The map shows almost all of them. There's a fine one near Down Tor, or if you want a really grand one climb up to Stalldown Barrow.

I walked along a single stone row near . . . .

. . . . on . . . .

There were about . . . . stones.

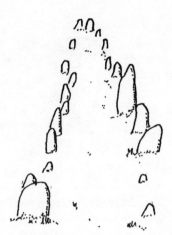

*Part of a double row on
Trowlesworthy Warren*

These are more fun than single rows because
you can walk between the stones and wonder if
the prehistoric people who set them up did the
same, and if they did, why did they? Look to see
if the stones are in opposite pairs, and if there
is a special one at the end. Are both ends the
same?

CLUES: Near Merrivale there are two double
rows close to each other.

I walked along a double stone row near . . . . . .

. . . . on . . . .

Beardown Man near Devil's Tor

Nobody knows who erected these huge stones, or why, or when, but they have certainly been standing where you see them for about 3,000 years. The finest are twice as high as a man, and the ones in wild and lonely places, like the Beardown Man pictured above, are especially impressive. Easier ones to visit would be the Longstone near the Merrivale rows, or the one to be seen from Kes Tor.

CLUES: On the map they are labelled as 'Standing stone' or 'Longstone'.

I inspected the menhir near . . . .

. . . . on . . . .

KISTVAEN

This one is near the shore of Fernworthy Reservoir

The Bronze Age people cremated their dead and buried the ashes in graves we now call Kistvaens. These are like a granite box dug into the soil and covered with a large slab. Earth was then heaped over everything. Nowadays these graves are all empty, so when you find one why not sit inside to get the feel of it?

CLUES: On the map they are called Cists. A small hole in the ground is hard to find so here are clues to two fairly easy ones. Visit the stone rows at Merrivale; or walk round Fernworthy Reservoir until you are opposite the fishing hut and near a small Rowan.

I sat in a kistvaen near . . . .

. . . . on . . . .

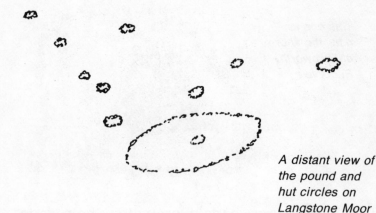

*A distant view of
the pound and
hut circles on
Langstone Moor*

A pound is an enclosure, like a small field, with
a granite wall around it. They were built to any
convenient size and shape wherever they were
needed. The oldest ones surround groups of
Bronze Age huts; others were intended for
folding sheep or gathering cattle. There are
many marked on the map, often well away from
any other walls.

CLUES: They are often more round than
square. Here are some names to set
you searching: Roundy Park, Round
Pound, Dunnabridge Pound.

I visited the pound near . . . .

. . . . on . . . .

QUARRY

*The largest
quarry at
Hay Tor*

There are plenty of tiny roadside quarries on the Moor where you can park a car, but for this book you should visit one of the big ones. The one at Merrivale is still operating and you cannot go in, but not far away, along a track, are Foggin Tor and Swell Tor quarries, where you can see some of the supports cut for London Bridge (No. 87). One of the best quarries is at Hay Tor, where there is a pond and some bits of old machinery (No. 98).

CLUES: Given above.

I visited the quarry at . . . .

. . . . on . . . .

23 | TARE AND FEATHER WORK

Tare
Feather

About the year 1800 a new way of splitting granite into blocks was introduced. A line of holes was drilled using a hammer and cold chisel (or 'jumper'). When the holes were about 10–12 cm deep an iron tare was inserted in each and wedged tightly with a couple of thinner 'feathers'. The tares were then hit in turn until the granite split along the line.

CLUES: Almost anywhere on the Moor you may come across a boulder showing a line of semicircular hollows along one edge.

I saw some tare and feather work at . . . .

. . . . on . . . .

Small blocks of granite, called setts, were once used to pave the roads in towns, and many thousands were made on Dartmoor during the second half of the last century. The sett maker worked at a bench called a banker. He made this from a few boulders set into a slope so that he could stand or kneel in front of it. Here with hammer and chisel he could make about 40 setts a day.

CLUES: Search the slope between Middle Staple Tor and the road.

I found a sett maker's banker near . . . .

. . . . on . . . .

25

A parish boundary stone

A warren boundary stone

A manor boundary stone

Stones were often set up to mark the boundaries of parishes, manors, mines, warrens or reservoirs. Some of the larger boundary stones have a name, date or initial carved on them. Visit one of this kind.

CLUES: The Haytor-Widecombe area is a good one to visit, but there are plenty more. Look for 'B.S.' on the map.

I visited the boundary stone near . . . .

. . . . on . . . .

On it was carved: . . . .

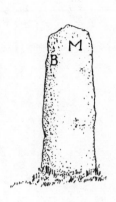

These were the forerunners of signposts. Some of the earliest have been in position for about 290 years. These usually bear just a single letter on each side indicating the town which that side faces. Sometimes the original track has disappeared so that the waymark seems to be in the middle of nowhere. When you find one of these you have to puzzle out what the letters stand for.

CLUES: Keep your eyes open near old crossroads.

On the waymark I found were the letters . . . . . .

. . . . They stand for . . . .

. . . . Date . . . .

Horn's Cross

Windy Post

In the days before maps, signposts, and good roads, finding a way across the Moor, especially in bad weather, was both difficult and dangerous. There were several well used tracks but on open ground it was easy to stray off them. So crosses were erected, often by monks, to act as guide posts. Some of these are still standing, and sometimes from one cross you can see the next one, but that is not very often. Every one has a name.

CLUES: They are all marked on the map, though this does not give their names.

I visited . . . . cross

near . . . . on . . . .

MILLSTONE

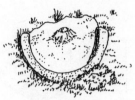

and this one
beside the
granite railway

This one is near Merrivale

Crushing apples, corn, or tin ore could all be done by milling. The moving stone would be turned by water or a horse. The millstones were cut to shape on the Moor and then transported to the mill. Sometimes a stone being cut would crack in the wrong place. Then it was abandoned or perhaps used for wall building. There are quite a lot left lying around.

CLUES: Walk along the track to Holwell quarry, or climb Rippon Tor, or search among the hut circles at Merrivale, or . . . .

I found a millstone near . . . .

. . . . on . . . .

GRANITE TROUGH

*A deep one
at Middleworth*

*and a shallow one
near Swell Tor*

Many troughs are in use on and near farms to provide drinking water for animals. Others may be found near a farm that has been abandoned. Sometimes you may come across one lying useless on a tor side. It must have been cut nearby from the moorstone (loose boulders of granite), but for some reason it was never carted away to be used.

CLUES: Watch where cattle gather, or look in a farmyard.

I found a granite trough near . . . .

. . . . on . . . .

A memorial to
a Queen's jubilee

and one to a girl
who died as a child

A memorial is made to last, so it is almost always a stone that has been prepared or specially set up in memory of a person or an event. It should have some writing on it, usually a name and a date. They are to be found in all shapes and sizes, and you may come across one in a surprising or even lonely place.

CLUES: Do not count gravestones, or boundary stones (No. 25).

I visited a memorial near . . . .

It said . . . .

. . . . on . . . .

A gert is a deep steep-sided gully cut into a hillside by tin miners. Most of them were dug between the 16th and early 19th centuries. When the miners found a good vein of tin ore (cassiterite) they followed it, digging their way along as far as possible. Sometimes gunpowder was used to break up the rocks.

If you explore a gert go carefully for some of the rocks may be loose and the sides are often slippery.

CLUES: An easy one to visit lies beside the road from Hexworthy to Sherberton. Others are to be seen down the slope from the Warren House Inn.

I visited a gert near . . . .

. . . . on . . . .

Blowing houses may once have looked something like this

A blowing house was a small workshop where tin ore was smelted (heated until the tin ran out of the rock). Water coming down a leat provided the power for working the bellows which blew the furnace, and operating the stamps which crushed the ore. See No. 33 for these.

You can often make out which way the leat came down, and decide where the wheel must have been.

CLUES: To find two good blowing houses walk down to O Brook foot from Saddle Bridge, cross the footbridge, and turn uphill.

I visited a blowing house near . . . .

. . . . on . . . .

MORTAR STONE

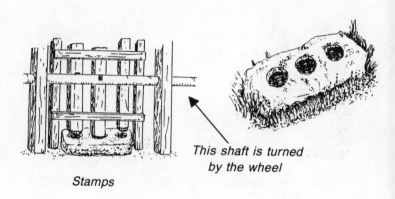

This shaft is turned by the wheel

Stamps

In a blowing house (No. 32) one of the important machines was a stamp to crush the tin ore to a powder. Two or three heavy beams, powered by a water wheel, pounded the ore in small hollows (mortars) in a block of granite. When the mortars became too deep to be useful the block was discarded. Look for these mortar stones at any blowing house you visit.

CLUES: Look in the blowing houses at O Brook foot or at Norsworthy. There is also a 'rescued' mortar stone at Venford Reservoir.

I found a mortar stone at . . . .

. . . . on . . . .

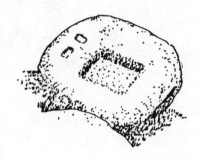

This mould stone at Gobbet blowing house has two sample moulds cut into it.

After the ore had been smelted in a blowing house (see No. 32) the liquid tin was run out into a mould, where it set into an ingot. Pure tin is so heavy that an ingot would weigh more than you do. Sometimes there is also a small sample mould cut into the stone. Mould stones are not nearly as common as mortar stones.

CLUES: Easy to visit blowing houses with mould stones are at Gobbet Mine near Hexworthy, and at O Brook foot.

I found a mould stone at . . . .

. . . . on . . . .

WHEELPIT

The wheels have gone. Only the pits are now left.

At some of the bigger mining sites huge wheels (the size of a house) were used to work the pumps which emptied water from the deeper levels. These wheels were connected by rods to one or more pumps, which might be some distance away. Sometimes the water was carried across an aqueduct and a wooden launder so that it could fall on to the wheel from above.

Take care when you are beside a deep wheelpit.

CLUES: There are good examples beside the tracks through Birch Tor Mine and Hexworthy Mine.

I inspected a wheelpit at . . . .

. . . . Mine on . . . .

This unusual pattern of long eared rabbits was an emblem used by the Dartmoor tinners. It may have had a magical meaning, or a religious one, or perhaps the tinners just liked rabbits (to eat!). Study the drawing to make sure the rabbits have the right number of ears. You can see this emblem inside the churches of Tavistock and Widecombe-in-the-Moor . . . .

CLUES: . . . but the easiest place to see them is outside the Warren House Inn.

I saw the tinners' rabbits at . . . .

. . . . on . . . .

FELSPAR

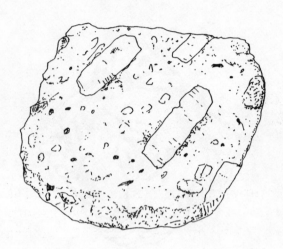

Felspar is one the main minerals of Dartmoor granite. It is usually a creamy colour, and forms a solid mass in which the other minerals are embedded. Sometimes it is quite pinkish. Quite often you can find giant crystals of felspar 2 or 3 cm long and oblong in shape. No other mineral in the granite has such big crystals, although quartz (No. 38) occurs in much larger masses. It is felspar that decomposes into China clay, or kaolin.

CLUES: Look on clean rock surfaces to find the big crystals.

I found some large felspar crystals near . . . . . .

. . . . on . . . .

QUARTZ

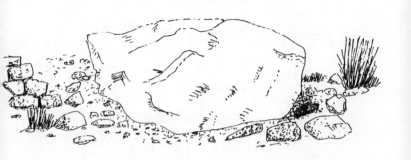

Quartz and Felspar (No. 37) are the two chief minerals in granite. Quartz is usually pale greyish white and very hard. Sometimes you come across large masses of it which are almost white, and if you look among piles of broken rock you will often find pocket sized white stones which are almost certain to be quartz. Collect one of these.

There are also two common black minerals in granite, but they are always in small crystals or patches. Mica has a shiny surface and its tiny flakes reflect the light. Tourmaline is much duller.

CLUES: A good place to collect rock samples is in the Plym by the last car park before Trowlesworthy Farm.

I found a lump of quartz near . . . .

. . . . on . . . .

LOGAN STONE

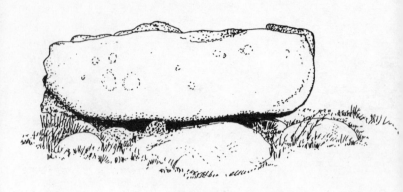

Logan stone on Smallacombe Rocks

To 'log' means to rock, and a logan stone is one that is too big to shift but which rocks if you push it. Through maybe millions of years its surface has been slowly eroded (worn away) and rounded off, and just by chance it now stands on its point of balance. But nothing in nature stays the same for ever, and at some time in the future a stone that logs now will change its shape, slip a little, and get stuck. Even some of the ones marked on the map don't log any more. But the one drawn above does.

CLUES: Just try your strength, or get a grown-up to do it for you.

I visited the logan stone near . . . .

. . . . and saw it log on . . . .

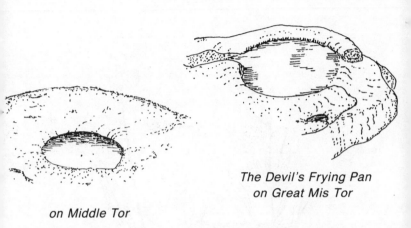

*The Devil's Frying Pan
on Great Mis Tor*

on Middle Tor

A rock basin starts life when a shallow pool of water collects on a flat-topped tor. Ever so slowly the water disolves the granite, frosts loosen minute particles, the sun dries it up, the wind blows away the dust, the pool fills again . . . and in ten thousand or a hundred thousand years the pool is a centimetre or so deeper. No one knows how long it takes. There are plenty of rock basins on the Moor up to 30 cm across. The biggest of all is on Kes Tor, and there is a fine one called The Devil's Frying Pan high up on Great Mis Tor.

CLUES: Climb up to any flat part of a tor.

I found a rock basin on . . . .

. . . . tor on . . . .

45

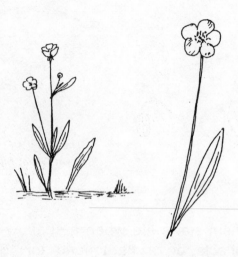

This yellow flower is very like a delicate buttercup, but the leaves are long and narrow. Their shape gives the plant its name. It nearly always grows by water, and sometimes in it.

You should be able to find it in almost any wet place during at least six months of the year. There is also a much larger plant called Greater Spearwort, but this does not grow on Dartmoor.

CLUES: Already given.

I found Lesser Spearwort . . . .

. . . . on . . . .

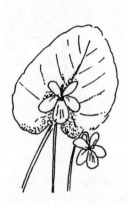

These are very common on Dartmoor and are among the earliest flowers to bloom in the Spring. They grow in much wetter places and have rounder leaves than the Violets of heath and hedgerow.

CLUES: Walk along a leat in Spring or Summer.

I found a Marsh Violet . . . .

. . . . on . . . .

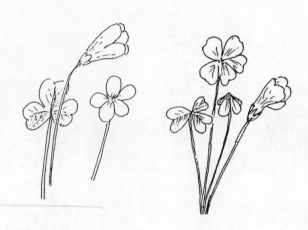

Although this dainty white flower is common in woodland it grows on the open moor as well. Look for it, in Spring, in places where there will be plenty of shade from boulders or taller plants later in the year. The leaves are very sensitive and close up at night or even in bright sunshine. They can be used to make a sauce, having a taste something like lemon. Why not taste a leaf or a flower? You may like it.

CLUES: Look under trees or among boulders.

I found a Wood Sorrel near . . . .

. . . . on . . . .

Here is a small flower that you will have no difficulty in finding, for it is widespread on the Moor. The petals are white but are decorated with yellow and purple spots. In days gone by the leaves of Eyebright were dried, powdered, and mixed into wine or beer. This medicine was then used as a cure for failing eye-sight. One writer said that if people made more use of this drink they would not need to go to an optician.

CLUES: You just need a bright eye!

I found Eyebright near . . . .

. . . . on . . . .

COTTONGRASS

Hare's-tail Cottongrass

Common Cottongrass

Here are two kinds of Cottongrass or Bog Cotton. Both species grow in wet acid places, and on the great upland bogs of the Moor they form a large part of the vegetation, gradually turning into peat. The Hare's-tail with just one head of cotton on each stalk is not nearly as common as the other Cottongrass.

CLUES: You will need waterproof footwear to walk where these grow.

I found . . . . Cottongrass near . . . . .

. . . . on . . . .

A stamen

You will certainly be in a wet place when you find one of these, for they are true bog plants. The flowers are yellow, and if you examine one closely you will see that the stalks of the stamens are clothed in a sort of orange-yellow wool. When the flowers are over the golden brown spikes of seed pods last a long time.

CLUES: Find a boggy place.

I found Bog Asphodel near . . . .

. . . . on . . . .

Glands on a leaf

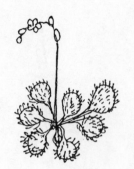

Many people expect carnivorous plants to be huge things with leaves or flowers ready to swallow small animals whole. But Sundew, the commonest of the moorland insectivorous plants, is not quite like that. The leaves are only about a centimetre across. They are covered with shiny, sticky glands, so that when a small insect lands on a leaf it gets stuck almost at once. The glands then slowly bend over to digest it. The flowers are white and need sunny weather to open.

CLUES: Look in boggy places among the Sphagnum moss.

I found a Sundew plant near . . . .

. . . . on . . . .

PALE BUTTERWORT

Each plant bears just one pale lilac flower on a stalk about 5 or 6 cm high. It grows only in wet, muddy places on acid soil. It is an insectivorous plant. When a small insect lands on a leaf it is held fast on the sticky surface, and the leaf edges slowly curl over to imprison and digest it.

CLUES: Look for it in late Summer in boggy or muddy places.

I found Pale Butterwort . . . .

. . . . on . . . .

*A cluster of
flowers beneath the leaves*

It won't take you long to find the leaves of Marsh Pennywort. It grows in wet places and is very common. The leaf stalks are only a few centimetres long, but no other plant has leaves this shape so close to the ground. (Look up also Wall Pennywort, No. 50). The real challenge is to find the tiny greenish white flowers. Look at the right-hand drawing.

CLUES: Bend down and search underneath the leaves in summer.

I found Marsh Pennywort in flower near . . . . . .

. . . . on . . . .

WALL PENNYWORT

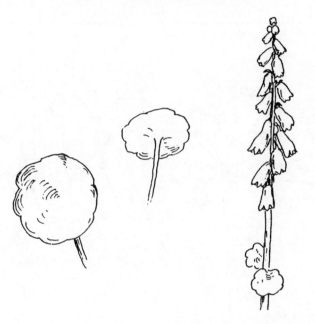

Marsh Pennywort and Wall Pennywort are the only two moorland plants that have round leaves joined to the stalk at their centre. This species almost always grows from cracks in walls or vertical rock faces. The flowers are a pale greenish cream colour. The plant is only frequent in the West Country.

(Marsh Pennywort is No. 49)

CLUES: Watch the walls and banks

I found Wall Pennywort near . . . .

. . . . on . . . .

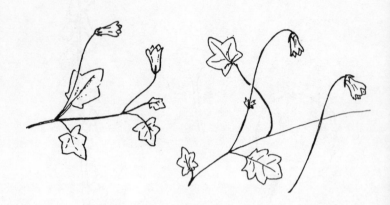

You will need sharp eyes to see these small blue flowers hiding in grassy places. Examine a leaf to see where the first part of the name comes from.

Except in Devon, Cornwall, and Wales this is a flower that is hardly ever seen, and even on Dartmoor you will not come across it very often.

CLUES: Look on grassy banks in damp places in summer.

I found Ivy-leaved Bellflower near . . . .

. . . . on . . . .

LOUSEWORT

 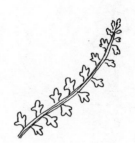

You can find Lousewort in flower during most of the spring and summer in damp grassy places, usually on a hillside. The flowers are pinkish.

The plant is so named because in olden times farmers said that cattle feeding on it would become infested with lice. The more likely truth is that the worms the animals caught are to be found in the same kind of place as Lousewort. But don't worry: you can't catch worms just by walking across Dartmoor.

CLUES: It's easier to find going uphill than down!

I found Lousewort . . . .

. . . . on . . . .

Bell Heather   *Cross-leaved Heath*   *Ling*

Three kinds of Heather grow on Dartmoor, and to complete this page you must find at least two of them on the same day. The first two above will be in flower from June until late September. Cross-leaved Heath has leaves in fours, paler, slightly larger flowers, and can grow in wetter places than Bell Heather. Ling has minute leaves, different shaped flowers, and blooms from July to October.

CLUES: Already given.

I found . . . .

and . . . . on . . . .

Flower

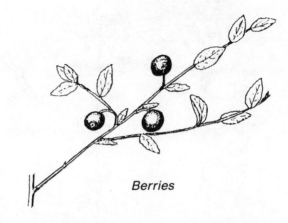

Berries

In other parts of England these have different names, such as Bilberry, Blueberry, or Blaeberry, but Dartmoor folk just call them Worts. A hundred and more years ago children used to gather them to sell at market, but this does not seem to happen any longer. But they are still good to eat. They go well in jelly, yoghurt, or a tart.

CLUES: Look for the flowers in June and taste the berries in August.

I tasted a Whortleberry near . . . .

. . . . on . . . .

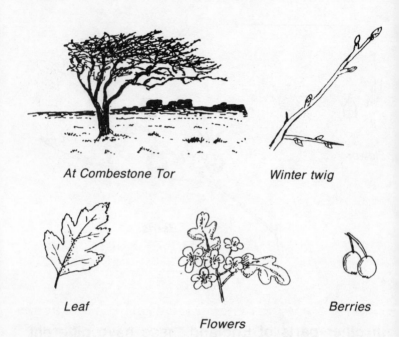

At Combestone Tor

Winter twig

Leaf

Flowers

Berries

You will probably pass a Hawthorn every time you walk on Dartmoor. In sheltered places they may bear a find crop of flowers or fruit, but on a tor or high windswept hillside leaves and thorns may be all they can manage. In such wild places they often grow into fantastic shapes, with a short, crooked trunk and branches bent away from the fiercest winds.

CLUES: Leaves and thorns.

I passed a Hawthorn near . . . .

. . . . on . . . .

ROWAN

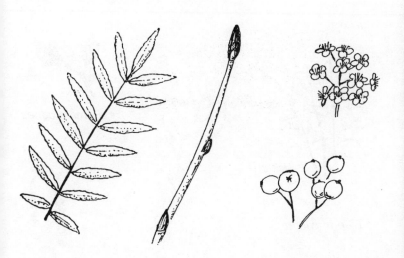

These are also called Mountain Ash because their leaves are similar to those of an Ash. Each leaf usually has 6 or 7 pairs of leaflets on one stalk. On the Ash the leaves and buds are also in pairs but on a Rowan these grow singly along the twigs. In sheltered places Rowans produce a mass of white flowers in late spring and red berries in late summer. But they also grow high on wind-swept tors where they may only have a few leaves.

CLUES: Leaves, buds, flowers, berries.

I saw a Rowan near . . . .

. . . . on . . . .

ALDER

Female cones

Tree in winter

Male catkins

Alders thrive best in wet soil, and are to be found along all the Dartmoor rivers in fairly sheltered places. They are easy to identify for the leaves are unlike those of any other tree. At any time of the year you will be able to find small woody cones among the twigs, and in spring there are catkins as well. Alder is one of the best woods for making shoes and gun-powder.

CLUES: Go for a riverside walk.

I found an Alder near the River . . . .

. . . . on . . . .

Cones

European Larch

Japanese Larch

Of all the conifers in the Dartmoor plantations Larches are the most interesting, for they are the only ones that have four colour changes— one for every season. In winter they are brown and leafless, in spring a bright pale green, in summer a richer mid-green, and in autumn yellowish as the leaves wither before falling.

Collect a few cones and examine them to see whether you have found a European Larch or a Japanese Larch.

CLUES: The leaves grow in tufts, and fall off in autumn.

I found some cones of . . . . Larch

at . . . . on . . . .

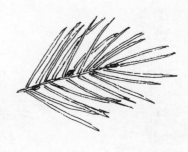

*A cone
and a close-up
showing the
3-fingered bracts*

Most of the large plantations of conifers on Dartmoor contain some Douglas Fir. The surest way to distinguish these from the Spruces is to find a cone. Only the Douglas has bracts with three little fingers at the tip.

CLUES: At Fernworthy look by the road just beyond SANDEMAN BRIDGE.

I found some Douglas Fir cones at . . . .

. . . . on . . . .

SITKA SPRUCE

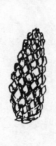

Sitka are common in all the coniferous plantations on Dartmoor. They grow fast and straight and are harvested when they are 50 to 60 years old and perhaps 20 m or more high. You can often identify them at a distance because the undersides of the needles have a strong blue tinge. If you feel them you will find they are much stiffer than other conifers. If in doubt look for a cone: these are about 7-8 cm long, quite a bit shorter than the Norway Spruce.

CLUES: Stiff bluish needles that are almost prickly.

I examined a Sitka Spruce . . . .

. . . . on . . . .

There are two woods on the Moor which are worth visiting because you will not find any others like them in Britain. These are Wistman's Wood and Black-a-tor Copse. They consist mainly of Oaks which have grown up among large boulders on a steep valley side. The boulders are covered with mosses and lichens, and the trees are stunted and twisted. Go slowly and with care when you explore beneath the trees.

CLUES: For Wistman's Wood start near Two Bridges, and for Black-a-tor Copse start from Meldon Dam.

I explored . . . .

. . . . on . . . .

66

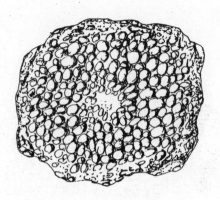

There are many different moorland and mountain lichens which grow flat on rock surfaces, and they are not always easy to identify. But here is one that has a 'different look' from all the others. Its colour depends on the weather, but normally it ranges from greenish through olive to brown. Its surface seems to be covered with flat bubbles. The kind of tripe that you can eat looks something like this.

CLUES: Look for it on rock faces, fairly high on the Moor.

I found some Rock Tripe near . . . .

. . . . on . . . .

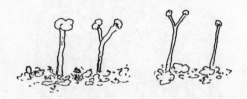

Dartmoor matchsticks are small lichens, about 2–3 cm high. They do grow on other heaths besides Dartmoor. They are greyish and at times bear tiny red blobs on their heads. These contain the spores which one day may be scattered and grow into new plants. Look for them on boulders and tree stumps as well as on the ground.

Some of the Pixy Cups (No. 64) also have these red blobs on top.

CLUES: Their name tells you the sort of thing to look for.

I found a Dartmoor Matchstick . . . .

. . . . on . . . .

PIXY CUP

Here is another little greenish-grey lichen to look out for. They are only a centimetre or so high, so would make a very small cup, even for a pixy!

Sometimes tiny red blobs grow round the edge of the cup. This is when they are in fruit. You may find them in woods as well as on the moor.

CLUES: Look among the mosses on tree stumps, banks, and boulders.

I found some Pixy Cups . . . .

. . . . on . . . .

69

BELTED GALLOWAY

The black cattle on the Moor are Galloways, and those with a broad white stripe round their middle are called Belted Galloways, or Belties. They are a hardy breed, without horns, and range far over the hills, their shaggy coat protecting them from all but the worst weather. But during the winter they will come down to the farm for shelter and extra food.

CLUES: You can hardly mistake a Beltie!

I saw some Belted Galloway . . . .

. . . . on . . . .

There are only a few small herds of these fine cattle on Dartmoor, so you won't see them very often. Their magnificent horns and shaggy golden-brown coats make them look fierce, but in fact the bulls are more docile than any other moorland breed. However, as in the case of all cattle, you should not approach a cow with a young calf. Highlanders are even hardier than Galloways and provide excellent beef, but almost no milk.

CLUES: Admire those horns!

I saw some Highland cattle near . . . .

. . . . on . . . .

These are the easiest kind of sheep to identify on Dartmoor. They are a hardy breed and spend most their life on the open moor. But during the worst of the winter they will come to shelter at the farm, especially at night. In winter too they will need extra feed. Both sexes have horns but the rams have a heavier pair than the ewes.

CLUES: The head is usually quite black, though sometimes it may be mottled like the legs.

I saw some Scottish Blackface . . . .

. . . . on . . . .

BADGER SETT

Footprint

You are not likely to see a Badger in daylight but there are plenty of setts in the National Park for you to look into. Most of them are in woodland on steep slopes, but there are quite a number on the open moor. The deep gullies left by the tinners are good places to explore. If you find what you think is a badger sett there should be several entrances and large piles of ex- cavated soil. Look for prints in the mud. If you find one that has 5 toes then it was certainly made by a badger.

CLUES: No luck? Then explore Hangman's Pit, near Combestone Tor.

I found a badger sett near . . . .

. . . . on . . . .

Bury rhymes with hurry

The open granite moorland is not a natural habitat for rabbits, but by heaping up piles of stones and earth in well drained places a suitable home could be made for them. These mounds are called buries or pillow mounds, and a number of them would form a warren. Some of the Dartmoor warrens lasted for hundreds of years and supplied rabbits to both miners and townsfolk.

A bury might be from 15 to 20 metres long and about 5 metres wide.

CLUES: Look for the words 'warren' or 'pillow mound' on the map.

I saw a rabbit bury on . . . .

. . . . Warren on . . . .

You will pass by many adders without seeing them because they slither away to safety when they feel or hear human feet approaching. But if you tread softly or jump down unexpectedly you may glimpse one. Look for them on sunny slopes for they like to bask in the sunshine.

You are not likely to tread on an adder, but if you are scrambling up a steep slope watch where you put your hands.

CLUES: Watch out on sunny days.

I saw and adder . . . .

. . . . on . . . .

75

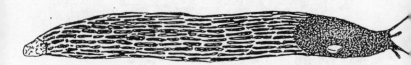

When the weather is to their liking, mild and damp, then these large slugs may appear in the open during the hours of daylight. You either see lots of them or none at all. This kind of slug is very different from the smaller grey ones that can be a pest in a garden, for they eat a great deal of decaying matter and so, like vultures and woodlice, they are part of nature's army of waste disposers.

CLUES: They like to come out after rain.

I saw a Great Black Slug near . . . .

. . . . on . . . .

When you put up a Snipe you will be on wet ground, for they spend most of their time in marshy places. They will fly away from you zigzagging for some distance. This makes them fairly easy to identify. They feed on worms and larvae using their long bills to probe into the mud. In spring you may hear one 'drumming'. They do this by spreading out two tail feathers and making short dives at the air. The feathers vibrate and make a humming or bleating sound. The nest is well hidden under a tussock of grass or heather.

CLUES: Watch for that zigzag.

I saw a Snipe . . . .

. . . . **on** . . . .

In size and shape these are very like the commoner Pied Wagtail, but the colours are grey and yellow. They live in lonelier places and spend most of their time by moorland streams. In winter they may fly down to the lowlands for a while.

CLUES: Watch quietly and you will see one hunting for small insects or snails in and by the water.

I watched a Grey Wagtail . . . .

. . . . on . . . .

78

DIPPER

These birds are great water lovers, and interesting ones to watch. On a stone in a stream they can often be seen bobbing up and down—that is why they are called Dippers. They are able to walk under the water where they search for insects, shrimps, and snails. They always nest close to running water, sometimes so close to a waterfall that the nest has an extra covering to protect it from splashes.

CLUES: Go quietly along a fast running stream.

I saw a Dipper by . . . .

. . . . on . . . .

HERON

Almost any river, reservoir, or quarry pond may give you a glimpse of a Heron, Dartmoor's largest bird. They are very wary so if you see one stand still and watch, or it will be up and away before you have had a good look. They come to the water to feed on fish, frogs, voles and beetles. Watch them stalking sedately through the shallows, and when they fly off notice how the neck is soon doubled back but the legs trail behind. Their nests may be some miles away, probably in a tall tree.

CLUES: Slow, powerful wingbeat and long legs.

I saw a heron . . . .

. . . . on . . . .

WHEATEAR

Although Wheatears spend the winter in Africa, south of the Sahara, they are back on Dartmoor by about the middle of March, and they will stay until late October. You will come across them all over the Moor, especially in rocky places. They are about sparrow size and build their nests in deep holes among boulders. The young birds can fly when they are just over a fortnight old.

CLUES: Look for the white rump as the Wheatear flies away.

I saw a Wheatear near . . . .

. . . . on . . . .

Only rarely will you see a perched buzzard, but you won't make many expeditions on Dartmoor without seeing one soaring above you head. With a wing span of over a metre they wheel round the sky gradually drifting away over the landscape. If you are near a nest—which may be in a tree—you may hear one mewing like a kitten as it flies above you. They feed on young rabbits, voles, lizards, large beetles, and even carrion.

CLUES: Just watch the sky.

I saw a Buzzard near . . . .

. . . . on . . . .

Ravens are the largest and blackest of the Crow family, and although they only nest on tors in the wildest parts of the Moor you may well see one or two scouring the hills from on high, without walking moor than half a mile from a road. They are superb fliers and sometimes put on fine displays of aerobatics. Listen for the very deep croak of the Raven—much deeper than Crow or Rook—as it flies overhead.

CLUES: Listen and look up.

I saw a Raven near . . . .

. . . . on . . . .

PROVING MORTAR

Making gunpowder used to be so dangerous that factories had to be built a long way from houses. The powder mills that stand well back from the road to the west of Postbridge are certainly in a lonely spot. Some of the buildings have been repaired and there are displays for you to visit. The little mortar was used to test the quality of the gunpowder by seeing how far a charge of powder would throw a cannonball.

CLUES: The mortar stands between the main road and the buildings.

I inspected the mortar at the Powder Mills on . .

. . . .

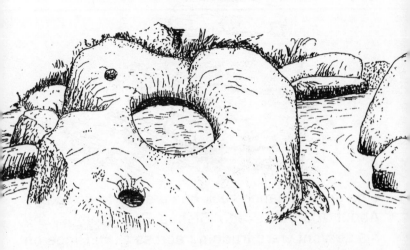

There is no other stone like this on Dartmoor. It is a large boulder through which a wide hole has been worn, probably by stones being whirled round in it when the river level was much higher. You should have no difficulty in sliding down through the hole on to the slab below. Parents used to pass their children through in order to cure them of whooping cough.

CLUES: It lies in the North Teign river close to its northern bank not far below Teign-e-ver Clapper.

I climbed through the Teign Tolmen . . . .

. . . . on . . . .

This queer-shaped rock has a story to go with it. About 700 years ago Bishop Branscombe and his servant were trudging across Corn Ridge on their way to Okehampton. They were tired and hungry. Presently a moorman in a long cloak and on horseback came up and offered them bread and cheese. Gratefully the bishop put out his hand to accept. But just at that moment the servant noticed that the stranger had goat's feet beneath his cloak, and he struck the food away. The stranger, who was of course the Devil, vanished. The loaf and cheese landed nearby and turned into two tiny tors.

CLUES: To get to Corn Ridge you could go up from Sourton or from Meldon Reservoir.

I walked round Branscombe's Loaf . . . .

. . . . on . . . .

BOWERMAN'S NOSE

This rock, which you will see on many picture postcards, is one of the most fantastic on Dartmoor. It is really just a miniature tor of unusual shape. An old legend tells that Bowerman was a mighty hunter who one day disturbed some witches while they were brewing spells. To get their revenge one of them turned herself into a hare. Bowerman chased the hare until he was so exhausted that he fell off his horse. The hare then changed back into a witch and turned the hunter into stone—and there he is.

CLUES: About a mile north of Hound Tor.

I walked all round Bowerman's Nose . . . .

. . . . on . . . .

A Cuckoo at Cuckoo Rock

Here is another mini tor with an interesting shape. It is not on a hilltop but on a slope to the southwest of Combshead Tor. The huge rock does not really look like a Cuckoo, but you can certainly hear and see these birds round here, where they probably lay their eggs in the nests of Meadow Pipits.

Underneath Cuckoo Rock is a small cave which, it is said, was once used to hide such things as smuggled brandy.

CLUES: A handy parking place would be at Norsworthy Bridge.

I walked all round Cuckoo Rock . . . .

. . . . on . . . .

Parliament Rock

For several hundred years the tin miners on Dartmoor had a parliament of their own to make laws and settle problems about their work. They used to meet on Crockern Tor because it was roughly the same distance from the three stannary (tin refining) towns of Tavistock, Chagford, and Ashburton, and also near a road. The members of the parliament had seats and a table, all made of flat boulders. There is still one large one left for you to find.

CLUES: Find Parliament Rock, then look around.

I visited Crockern Torn Tor and found . . . .

. . . . on . . . .

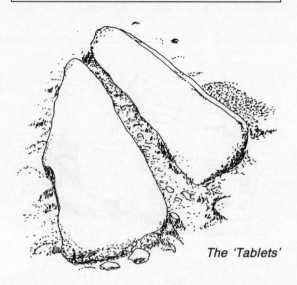

The 'Tablets'

Near the top of Buckland Beacon are two slabs of granite which have been 'dressed' on one face to give a flat surface. On these are carved the Ten Commandments, so that in a way they are like the tablets of the law that Moses obtained on another mountain. The lettering took one man 5 weeks to do during the summer of 1928.

The Beacon is one of the hills where signal fires were lit on the approach of the Spanish Armada.

CLUES: Read line one again.

I saw the Ten Commandments stones on Buck-

land Beacon on . . . .

THE COFFIN STONE

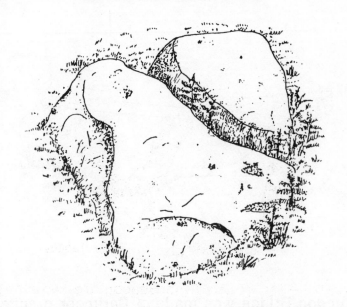

Once coffins had to be carried to church on men's backs because carts could not be handled across the rough moorland. About half way up the steep hill from Dartmeet to Widecombe is a low boulder split into two. When coming this way to church a coffin would be set down here for a short rest. There are several sets of initials and some crosses carved on it in memory of the dead who rested there.

CLUES: It lies by a path through the bracken, to the south of the road.

On the Coffin Stone I saw these initials . . . . . .

. . . . on . . . .

BRIDGE CORBELS

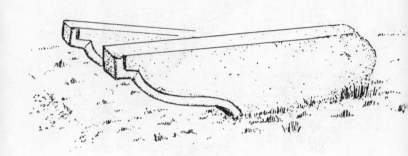

London Bridge was made of Dartmoor granite. Some of the stone came from Hay Tor Quarry and some from Foggin Tor or Swell Tor. The corbels, or brackets of stone, were cut to support a path along one side of the bridge. These are some spare ones that were left behind. A wider bridge has now been built to replace the old one, and the bridge of Dartmoor granite has been sent to the U.S.A. and rebuilt in Arizona.

CLUES: Walk along an old railway beneath Swell Tor.

I inspected the corbels for London Bridge and

counted . . . . on . . . .

Loco shed

A military target railway

There aren't any working railways left now on Dartmoor, but at various times quite a few were operating to carry passengers, clay, granite, peat, machinery, building materials, and even army targets. Most of the rails have gone, except the granite ones on the Hay Tor line, but you can still find odd bolts, sleepers, milestones, bridges, points and levers. The little railway above is still complete and you can walk from end to end in about 5 minutes.

CLUES: Start at the end of the army road under West Mill Tor.

I walked along an old railway near . . . .

. . . . on . . . .

. . . and this is
No. 3458

This is No. 3457 . . .

These concrete pillars, often called Trig points are always put on a hilltop with a wide view. Cartographers (map-makers) fix their instruments to them when surveying. Each one has a metal plate on one face giving a reference number. On the map every one is marked by a little triangle, and its height is given.

CLUES: Look up. If you see a person on a tor who stands very still he may be a trig point!

I climbed up to the trig point on . . . .

. . . . on . . . .

Its number was . . . .

DANGER
MERRIVALE RANGE
DO NOT PASS THE LINE
OF RED AND WHITE POSTS
WHILE A FLAG OR
LAMP IS FLYING FROM
THE HIGH GROUND TO THE
FRONT OF THIS BOARD.
DO NOT TOUCH ANY
METAL OBJECT IT
MAY EXPLODE.

Before you get on to firing range or reach a red flag or come up to the smaller red and white posts that mark the range boundaries you sometimes see a notice board like the one above. If there is no red flag on the hill beyond then you can safely continue, but if a flag is flying look round to where the poles run and do not cross their line.

CLUES: Check any notice board you see.

I read the range notice board near . . . .

. . . . on . . . .

OBSERVATION POST

Lookout on Steeperton Tor

The firing range that runs south from Okehampton camp covers about 18 square miles of moorland, and scattered across it are a number of strongly built observation posts. Some stand on open ground near the military road, others shelter under the side of a tor. Many of them have a number painted on the front. O.P.15 is a favourite starting point for the walk to Cranmere Pool.

CLUES: Take the loop road running south from Okehampton Camp.

I inspected the observation post at . . . .

. . . . on . . . .

It was Number . . . .

The highest triangulation pillar, flag pole, and observation post in Devon are all on Yes Tor.

There are three firing ranges on northern Dartmoor where live ammunition is used. Round the range boundaries are 25 flagpoles on which red flags are flown when firing is in progress. They are almost all on hilltops and are easily seen. The flags are hoisted by 10 a.m. at the latest if firing is to take place at all that day, and are lowered as soon as it is over. Moorland post offices have a list of firing days and times.

If a red flag is flying do not go up to the pole. It might be inside the boundary.

CLUES: Not needed! But read also No. 90.

I touched the flagpole on . . . .

. . . . on . . . .

A hut at Holwell Quarry

There are quite a lot of tiny ruined buildings on the Moor once used by shepherds, stone-masons, tinners, and peatcutters. Some, like the beehive huts were just used as storage, others were workshops, and some were used as homes. It is rare to find one that still has a roof. Usually there is just an oblong of tumbledown walls. A few of these huts are high on the open moor, and it's quite a puzzle to think why they are there.

CLUES: They may be almost anywhere. Make sure as far as you can that the one you find is not a blowing house (No. 32) or a hut circle (No. 15).

I found a ruined hut near . . . .

. . . . on . . . .

There are 365 square miles of the Dartmoor National Park, and the rangers who take care of it are busy people. Animals, people, cars, trees, crops, walls, gates, paths, bridges, streams, leats, historical remains . . . all need looking after. Wind, floods, and snow cause problems: so do animals, cars, and people!

There are seven rangers, each with his or her own part of the Moor to patrol, so it won't be long before you spot one.

CLUES: In the information centres you can get a free newspaper where you will find the rangers' photographs.

I saw a ranger's vehicle number . . . .

near . . . . on . . . .

Here is the only thing in this book that you can 'find' by standing still and waiting for it to walk past you! When letterboxers have collected 100 'stamps' they can join a club and wear a badge like the one above. These are often sewn on their rucksacks. Letterboxers always carry a map and compass and are well protected against bad weather and wet grass.

CLUES: Watch those rucksacks.

I saw a letterboxer wearing a 100 Club badge

near . . . .

. . . . on . . . .

There are hundreds of 'letterboxes' and thousands of 'box-hunters' out on the Moor. Each box contains a visitors' book and a rubber stamp. They are well hidden and are not to be found along a well used track. When you find one press the stamp in the space above, and then hide everything away very carefully just where you found it.

CLUES: You have to use your eyes and brains, and think. Where would you hide a small box?

Name of box . . . .

Place . . . .

Date . . . .

There is a car park near each of these bridges

From the 18th century onwards a number of roads across the Moor have been improved, and new bridges built to replace the old clappers and fords. Most of these bridges are still in use, although some have been banned to coaches and caravans. Several of them bear a plaque which tells you when they were built.

CLUES: Look on both faces of any bridge that carries a road.

I saw a plaque on . . . .

Bridge on . . . . The writing on it

said: . . . .

OLD MACHINERY

An old winch in Hay Tor quarry

Miners, quarrymen, and railway builders have left behind all sorts of interesting bits and pieces of machinery, tools, and transport.

Under this heading you could count such things as the concrete base of a crane, the leg of a derrick, a buddle, anchor rings for cables, bits of winding gear, railway bolts, nails, wheels, axles, girders, pipes . . . almost anything to do with engineering that you find on the Moor.

CLUES: Quarries and mining sites make good hunting grounds.

I found . . . .

near . . . . on . . . .

This one is on Black Ridge

On the blanket bog of northern Dartmoor walking can be very tiring, and for a rider on horseback some hills cannot be crossed at all. So round about 1900 a number of passes were dug through the peat until a firm surface was reached. Later on memorial stones to Frank Phillpotts, who had these passes dug, were placed at the ends of many of them.

CLUES: The passes are marked on the map, but read the warning on page 4 before you set out to find one.

I walked through a Phillpotts peat pass . . . .

. . . . on . . . .

The highest cairn in southern England

In all Dartmoor only two tors rise to over 2,000 feet: High Willhays at 2,037 feet (621m) and Yes Tor at 2,030 feet (619m). You can easily visit both of them in a half day excursion, for the road from Okehampton Camp will take you as far as the foot of West Mill Tor, and from there on there is a track for much of the way. When you stand on High Willhays you will be higher than anyone else in southern England. There is a small cairn on the summit, so if you put another stone on top of it you will make the highest point on Dartmoor even higher!

CLUES: Go through the gate at the camp and turn right before the ford.

I climbed up to . . . .

. . . . on . . . .

Perhaps you have found ninety nine of the things in this book, and there's just one which is too difficult, like a peat pass, or too uncertain, like a Raven, or too far away from you home, or impossible because winter has come.

So here is a chance to make your century. Choose one more of your own which you enjoyed finding, and put it on this page.

I found . . . .

. . . . on . . . .

PROGESS CHART

1	2	3	4	5	6	7	8	9	10
11	12	13	14	15	16	17	18	19	20
21	22	23	24	25	26	27	28	29	30
31	32	33	34	35	36	37	38	39	40
41	42	43	44	45	46	47	48	49	50
51	52	53	54	55	56	57	58	59	60
61	62	63	64	65	66	67	68	69	70
71	72	73	74	75	76	77	78	79	80
81	82	83	84	85	86	87	88	89	90
91	92	93	94	95	96	97	98	99	100
101									

Colour in each square when you have
found that number.

On the next two pages
there is room to put
some things of your own choice.

INDEX

to Box numbers (not pages)

111